Bianca
Learns the Lord's Prayer

Written and Illustrated by
Curt Gledhill

ISBN 978-1-63784-084-9 (paperback)
ISBN 978-1-63784-085-6 (digital)

Hawes & Jenkins Publishing
16427 N Scottsdale Road Suite 410
Scottsdale, AZ 85254
www.hawesjenkins.com

Printed in the United States of America

Acknowledgements

I want to thank my wife for her tireless support of my artwork, ideas, and the years it took to complete this book. God is my rock, but she is the mortar that keeps me attached to Him.

How this book came to be

My four-year old daughter asked about the Lord's Prayer after church one Sunday. I gave her the quick "dad" answer and then thought it would be nice to find a children's book that explained more in terms in which she and other children could understand and relate. When I could not find a book like that, I decided to make one myself. I spent time planning and sketching out a variety of ideas on how the concept could be presented, but did not come up with anything that would work. Then God woke me up at about two in the morning with a clear picture of these characters and the bones of a story.

After numerous edits, rewrites, and restarts, this is the result: *Bianca Learns the Lord's Prayer*. I sincerely hope this book begins an ongoing conversation between your children and their Heavenly Father.

Our Father, who art in heaven…
The minister began the prayer that Bianca had heard so many times. She could hear all of the people in the church saying the prayer with the minister. Bianca also said the parts she knew, but had not learned the whole prayer yet.

1

Bianca was with her grandfather. She called him Papa. They stood together under the last pew on the left, near the back of the church, as always. This was an evening church service and Bianca was spending some special time on her own with Papa.

2

Church ended shortly after the prayer and, as the rest of the people filed out of the church, Papa got out a broom to begin cleaning up after the service.

Papa and Nana lived here in the church. Their job was to keep the church clean. Nana was visiting her sister this weekend, so Bianca was spending the night at the church to help Papa. She liked to help him clean the church.

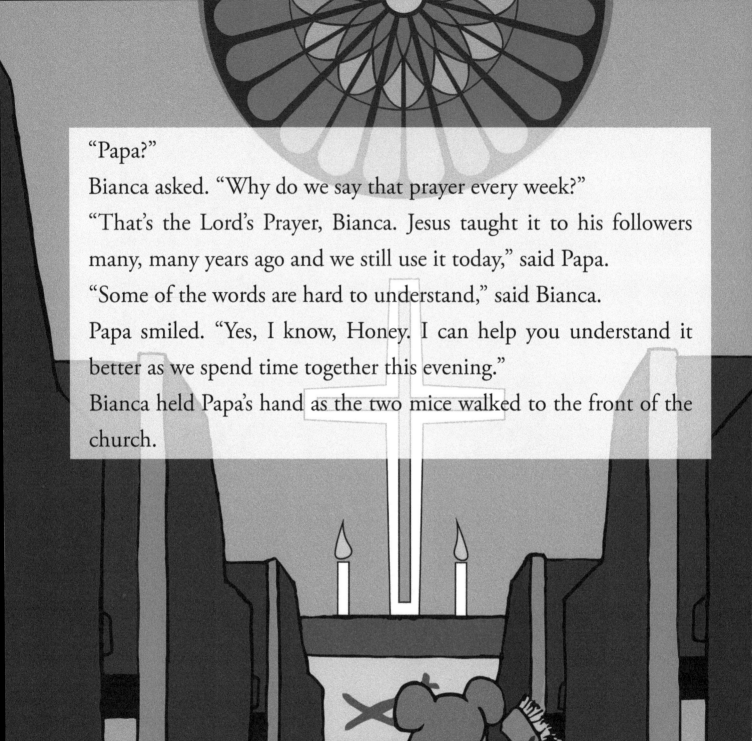

"Papa?"

Bianca asked. "Why do we say that prayer every week?"

"That's the Lord's Prayer, Bianca. Jesus taught it to his followers many, many years ago and we still use it today," said Papa.

"Some of the words are hard to understand," said Bianca.

Papa smiled. "Yes, I know, Honey. I can help you understand it better as we spend time together this evening."

Bianca held Papa's hand as the two mice walked to the front of the church.

To get all the way up to the altar, the two mice had to climb up on a chair and jump to the altar. It was a little bit like going to a playground.

6

They began to move
money from the
offering plate to a
special box to be
counted later. Papa
could carry six coins
at a time! Bianca
could only carry one.

"Many of the words we say in the Lord's Prayer are older words that we don't hear anymore. We still use them in this prayer because they help remind us of how long Christians have been saying the prayer."

Papa helped Bianca with her coin and then put his coins into the box.

When he had finished with the coins, Papa continued. "The Christians that learned the prayer before us, passed it on to us. Someday, when you have a family, you will pass it on to your children and maybe even your grandchildren."

Bianca smiled as she imagined someday being surrounded by her own grandchildren, as she taught them the prayer.

Bianca looked up at Papa. "I know how it starts: *Our Father, who art in heaven, hallowed be thy name.*" That means that even though God is all the way up in heaven, he is still the father of all of us. He loves and cares for us better than anyone else can."

Then Bianca got a puzzled look on her face. "I'm not really sure what hallowed means, though."

"Well, Bianca, you've got a really good start on the first part. Hallowed means holy. So, we are really saying holy is your name. This means we put God above all else and want others to show the same respect." Papa handed Bianca a cleaning cloth.

"Momma says some people use God's name when they are not praying, but when they are angry, instead," said Bianca. "She says that makes God sad."

"Your Momma is correct, Bianca. It's important that we treat God with the respect he deserves and speak well about him to others," replied Papa. He began shining up the bottom of the candle sticks.

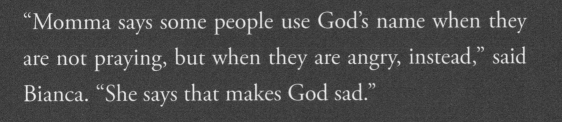

Bianca held a ladder up against one of the candles while Papa climbed up. At the top, he blew out the candle and then continued. "When we say *thy kingdom come*, we are asking that God give us the blessing of being a part of his plan here on Earth."

Then she said, "On Thursdays, I go with Mom and Dad to help pass out food to people that need it. Isn't that like helping God's kingdom come and being part of his plan?"

14

"Yes, Bianca," said Papa. "That is a good example. There are also lots of other things we can do to help God's kingdom come. We can share clothing, or money, or even just talking to someone that needs a friend. All of these things help God's kingdom come because they show God's love to all people."

"When we say *thy will be done on Earth as it is in heaven*," continued Papa, "we are telling God that we know heaven is perfect, but that Earth is no longer perfect because of sin. Many people do not love God anymore and do not try to obey him. We can help God's will be done by doing all that God asks and encouraging others to do the same."

Papa climbed down from putting out the candles.

Bianca and Papa were done cleaning for the night. They went to the little mouse door in the corner and went in for the night. This is where Nana and Papa lived. Bianca loved it here because it was quiet and warm and always smelled of cookies.

Now it was time for dinner and Papa was making Bianca's favorite—grilled cheese sandwiches!

Bianca helped Papa by setting the table. Papa said a short prayer asking God to bless the meal, to give thanks for the time he and Bianca were sharing, and asked God to keep Nana safe on her trip.

After she said "Amen," Bianca picked up her sandwich. She took a big gooey bite as Papa continued explaining the prayer.

"The next part is about what we are doing right now—eating!" Papa said with a smile. "When we pray *give us this day our daily bread*, we are trusting God to give us what we need. We don't really need that much to stay alive, yet God gives us that and so much more."

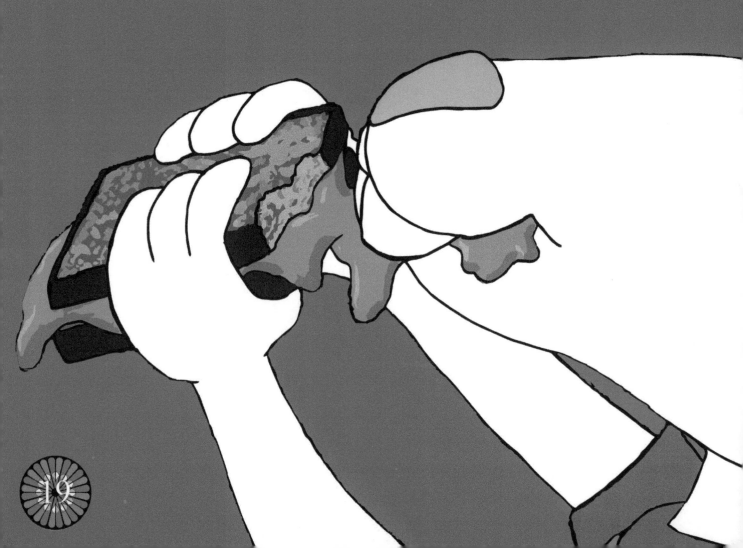

"Like a family, and a cozy place to live, and gooey grilled cheese sandwiches to eat!" said Bianca excitedly.

"That's right," laughed Papa. "He gives us so many blessings every day that we could never count them all."

BLESS
~THIS~
HOUSE

When Papa and Bianca had finished the sandwiches, they began to gather up the dishes.

"The next part of the prayer is *and forgive us our trespasses as we forgive those that trespass against us.* Trespass means to go somewhere we are not supposed to go. It means to sin against God and others. We are asking God to forgive us our sins and asking for help to forgive those that sin against us."

21

"That's not always easy to do," admitted Bianca, as she dried a dish with her towel. "Sometimes I get mad at my little brother when he breaks my crayons. I have trouble forgiving him, even if it was an accident."

"Sometimes it is difficult to forgive, Bianca," said Papa, "but this part of the prayer reminds us that God forgives us all the time, so we need to try to do the same to others. God loves us so much that he never gives up on us. All we need to do is ask."

Papa looked carefully at a glass he had washed to make sure it was clean.

Bianca smiled. It felt good to know that God's forgiveness was always there for her, no matter what.

Then Papa continued, "The next part of the prayer is *and lead us not into temptation.* Temptation is when something happens that makes us want to sin. It is like when I tell the doctor that I will not eat so many cookies, but then I get home and Nana has some fresh ones coming out of the oven. They smell so good that I want to have one, even though the doctor said I should not. That's temptation. We need God's strength because our own strength is not always enough."

Papa and Bianca finished the dishes and went out into the church again. Papa liked to sit and watch the moon rise and pass behind the big rose window at the front of the church. Bianca liked it too. She thought that when the light came through the window and showed the beautiful colors, it was as if God himself was looking down at her. Because of that, Papa made sure the window was always clean.

As they sat looking at the window, Papa continued, "*But deliver us from evil,* is asking God to protect us. There are many bad things and bad people in this world that can hurt us. We know God is stronger than all of them. We might still have bad things happen to us, but we are asking God to help get us through those challenges."

Bianca snuggled up a little tighter to Papa. She loved the rose window, but when the rest of the church was so dark, it could be a little scary. Just below the rose window, was a cross. The cross reminded her that Jesus died to save her. This helped Bianca know she was safe tonight and every night.

Then Bianca jumped up. "I know how it ends!" she said. "*For thine is the kingdom and the power and the glory forever and ever. Amen.* That's the part I always remember."

"Great job, Bianca" said Papa, his arms stretched wide. "The last part is our way of praising God and announcing to everyone around us that God is in control. He has more power than anyone or anything else. Some churches say that last part a little differently, but it all means the same thing."

"What's that?" asked Bianca.

Papa got a big grin on his face.

"That God—is—GREAT!"

Bianca smiled wide at Papa's words and threw her arms around his neck in a big hug. "Thank you for explaining the prayer to me, Papa." Then Bianca got a worried look on her face. "Is this the only prayer I can say from now on?" she asked.

"Not at all, Bianca," Papa reassured her. "God wants us to speak to him about anything at any time. He wants us to simply say what is on our minds and in our hearts. We can ask him for help or just tell him we loved the sunrise that day. We can ask for forgiveness for anything. We can pray that he lets us be a part of his plans on Earth. He just wants us to talk to him because he loves us."

"So praying to God can be just talking to him—like you and I are doing right now!" Bianca exclaimed.

"Exactly," said Papa. "The Lord's Prayer is just an example. It is a way to pray and it is a reminder of all of the things that God wants us to talk to him about. It gives us a common prayer that all Christians can say as one family under God."

With that, Papa stood up and looked around the church once more. "I think it's a little past your bedtime," he said with a twinkle in his eye. Bianca smiled at that. She often got to stay up just a little later when she came to Nana and Papa's house.

Bianca changed into her pajamas and climbed into the teacup bed that she used when she came to visit. "Can we say it once more together this time, Papa? I think I can remember all of the parts."

So the two mice folded their
hands and closed their eyes.
"*Our Father, who art in heaven*
Hallowed be thy name
Thy kingdom come
Thy will be done on Earth
as it is in heaven.
Give us this day our daily bread
And forgive us our trespasses As we
forgive those who trespass against us
And lead us not into temptation
But deliver us from evil
For thine is the kingdom
and the power and the
glory forever and ever.
Amen"

Papa then kissed her forehead
and said good night. He stepped
out of the room and closed the
door most of the way.

Bianca turned toward a little
window in her room that faced
out into the church. From here
she could see the rose window
and it was all lit up.

As the colored light fell across her face, Bianca thought of the window as God's eye again. She had a smile on her face as she remembered when Papa said,

"God—is—GREAT!"

38

And then Bianca thought she saw a little twinkle in the middle of the window. As she closed her eyes, she was pretty sure that tonight, God was smiling, too.

The End

Bianca is a small mouse with a big heart. She wants to learn the Lord's Prayer. She is staying at her Papa's at the church, where he lives as a caretaker. As they clean the church, make a meal, clean up, and finally Bianca heads to bed, Papa talks through all the parts of the prayer and the meaning behind it.

About the Author/Illustrator

After graduating from the University of Michigan School of Art, Curt spent a few years as a graphic designer before becoming a teacher. He has been an art teacher in the public school system in a small town in Michigan for over twenty years. Gledhill lives in Michigan with his wife, two children, and a red lab named Hudson.

Printed in the USA
CPSIA information can be obtained
at www.ICGtesting.com
LVHW061011210324
775117LV00027B/231

9 781637 840849